The Wide-Mouthed Frog

Down in the swamp there lived a wide-mouthed frog.

One day he was sitting in the sun, when along came a butterfly.

3

"What are you?"
asked the wide-mouthed frog.

"I'm a butterfly," said the butterfly.
"What are you?"

"I'm a WIDE-MOUTHED FROG and I eat butterflies."

Along came a grasshopper.

"What are you?"
asked the wide-mouthed frog.

"I'm a grasshopper,"
said the grasshopper.

"What are you?"

"I'm a WIDE-MOUTHED FROG and I eat grasshoppers."

Along came a snake.

"What are you?"
asked the wide-mouthed frog.

"I'm a SNAKE, and I
eat wide-mouthed frogs."

"Are **you** a wide-mouthed frog?"

"Oh no!"
croaked the wide-mouthed frog.

15

"You don't find them around here any more."